THE ULTIMATE KANSAS CITY ROYALS TRIVIA BOOK

A Collection of Amazing Trivia Quizzes and Fun Facts for Die-Hard Royals Fans!

Ray Walker

978-1-953563-52-1

CONTENTS

INTRODUCTION

The Kansas City Royals were established in 1969. Since their induction into the MLB as an expansion team, they have consistently proven themselves to be a team who fights hard and is a force to be reckoned with in the MLB.

They currently hold two World Series championships, which they won in 1985 and 2015. They have also won four American League pennants, one Central division title, 10 West division titles, and one Wild Card berth. They are very often a threat in the American League Central Division, having last won it in 2015, the same year they made their most recent World Series appearance.

The Royals currently call Kauffman Stadium home, which opened in 1973. They play in one of the most difficult divisions in baseball, the American League Central alongside the Minnesota Twins, Chicago White Sox, Cleveland Indians, and Detroit Tigers.

The thing about baseball is it's a lot like life. There are good times and bad times, good days, and bad days, but you have to do your absolute best to never give up. The Kansas City Royals have proven that they refuse to give up and that they will do anything they need to do in order to bring a championship to the state of Missouri.

Winning is more than possible when you have a storied past like the Kansas City Royals do. They have such a captivating history and so many undeniable player legacies to be profoundly proud of. Especially considering the numbers already retired by the Royals: George Brett, Dick Howser, Frank White, and, of course, Jackie Robinson.

With such a storied team past that goes back generations, you're probably already very knowledgeable as the die-hard Royals fan that you are. Let's test that knowledge to see if you truly are the world's biggest Royals' fan, keeping in mind the information is accurate up to the 2020 season.

CHAPTER 1:

ORIGINS & HISTORY

QUIZ TIME!

1. Which of the following team names did the Royals franchise once go by?
   a. Kansas City Monarchs
   b. Kansas City Athletics
   c. Kansas City Chiefs
   d. They have always been the Royals.
2. In what year was the Kansas City Royals franchise established?
   a. 1955
   b. 1959
   c. 1961
   d. 1969
3. The Royals' current home stadium is Kauffman Stadium.
   a. True
   b. False

4. Which division do the Kansas City Royals play in currently?

   a. American League West
   b. American League Central
   c. National League West
   d. National League Central

5. The Kansas City Royals have never won a Wild Card berth.

   a. True
   b. False

6. How many American League pennants have the Kansas City Royals franchise?

   a. 1
   b. 2
   c. 4
   d. 6

7. What is the name of the Kansas City Royals' mascot?

   a. King Slugger
   b. Sluggerrr
   c. Paws
   d. Stomper

8. Who is the winningest manager in Kansas City Royals?

   a. Dick Howser
   b. Whitey Herzog
   c. John Wathan
   d. Ned Yost

9. What is the name of the Kansas City Royals' Triple A-Team, and where are they located?
   a. Nashville Sounds
   b. Fresno Grizzlies
   c. Omaha Storm Chasers
   d. Jacksonville Jumbo Shrimp
10. Who was the first manager of the Royals franchise?
   a. Charlie Metro
   b. Joe Gordon
   c. Whitey Herzog
   d. Bob Lemon
11. The Kansas City Royals were members of the American League West Division from 1969 to 1993.
   a. True
   b. False
12. What is the name of the Royals' current spring training home stadium?
   a. Hohokam Stadium
   b. Salt River Fields at Talking Stick
   c. Surprise Stadium
   d. Tempe Diablo Stadium
13. How many appearances has the Kansas City Royals franchise made in the MLB playoffs?
   a. 7
   b. 8
   c. 9
   d. 11

14. How many World Series titles have the Kansas City Royals?

    a. 1
    b. 2
    c. 3
    d. 4

15. The Kansas City Royals' current manager is Mike Matheny.

    a. True
    b. False

16. Which stadium was the first home of the Kansas City Royals franchise?

    a. Athletic Park
    b. Exposition Park
    c. Kauffman Stadium
    d. Municipal Stadium

17. Who is the current general manager of the Kansas City Royals?

    a. Mike Rizzo
    b. Dayton Moore
    c. David Forst
    d. David Stearns

18. How many American League Central division titles have the Kansas City Royals won?

    a. 0
    b. 1

c. 2
d. 3

19. The Kansas City Royals won six American League West championships during their time in that division.

    a. True
    b. False

20. The Royals were named after the American Royal livestock show, which has been held in Kansas City since 1899.

    a. True
    b. False

QUIZ ANSWERS

1. D – They have always been the Royals.
2. D – 1969
3. A – True
4. B – American League Central
5. B – False (They won a berth in 2014.)
6. C – 4
7. B – Sluggerrr
8. D – Ned Yost
9. C – Omaha Storm Chasers
10. B – Joe Gordon
11. A – True
12. C – Surprise Stadium
13. C – 9
14. B – 2
15. A – True
16. D – Municipal Stadium
17. B – Dayton Moore
18. B – 1 (2015)
19. A – True
20. A – True

DID YOU KNOW?

1. The Kansas City Royals franchise has had 20 managers so far in their history. They include: Joe Gordon, Charlie Metro, Bob Lemon, Jack McKeon, Whitey Herzog, Jim Frey, Dick Howser, Mike Ferraro, Billy Gardner, John Wathan, Bob Schaefer, Hal McRae, Bob Boone, Tony Muser, John Mizerock, Tony Peña, Buddy Bell, Trey Hillman, Ned Yost, and Mike Matheny.
2. The Kansas City Royals' current manager is Mike Matheny. He previously managed the St. Louis Cardinals for seven seasons. He played in the MLB for 13 seasons as a catcher for the Milwaukee Brewers, San Francisco Giants, Toronto Blue Jays, and St. Louis Cardinals. He is also a 4x Gold Glove Award winner. He has been the Royals' manager since 2020.
3. Ned Yost is the Kansas City Royals' all-time winningest manager with a record of 746-839 (.471). He also managed the Milwaukee Brewers in his coaching career. During his playing career as a catcher, he played for the Milwaukee Brewers, Montreal Expos, and Texas Rangers. Yost managed the Kansas City Royals from 2010 to 2019.
4. John Sherman is the current owner of the Kansas City Royals. He is the founder and former CEO of Inergy LP. He also bought a minority share of the Cleveland Indians in 2016 and became their vice chairman. The Kansas City

Royals were founded by Ewing Kauffman, who was a pharmaceutical businessman from Kansas City.

5. The Kansas City Royals have hosted two MLB All-Star Games so far in franchise history. The first one took place in 1973 at Kauffman Stadium and the second in 2012 at Kauffman Stadium.
6. The Kansas City Royals have had four no-hitters thrown in franchise history. The first occurred in 1973, thrown by Steve Busby, and the latest occurred in 1991, thrown by Bret Saberhagen. There has never been a perfect game thrown in Kansas City Royals history.
7. When choosing a name for the Royals franchise, it was determined that it meshed well with other professional sports team names in Kansas City including the Kansas City Chiefs of the NFL, the former Kansas City Kings of the NBA (now the Sacramento Kings), and the former Kansas City Monarchs of the Negro National League.
8. The Royals' Double-A team is the Northwest Arkansas Naturals. High Single-A is the Quad City River Bandits. Low Single-A is the Columbia Fireflies.
9. The Royals' mascot, Sluggerrr the lion, debuted in 1996.
10. The Royals have not retired a player's number since they retired Frank White's number 20 in 1995.

CHAPTER 2:

JERSEYS & NUMBERS

QUIZ TIME!

1. The Royals began wearing pullover uniforms in 1973. Their buttoned jerseys made a return in 1983.

   a. True
   b. False

2. What are the Kansas City Royals' official team colors?

   a. Powder blue, gold, and white
   b. Royal blue, gold, and white
   c. Royal blue, powder blue, gold, and white
   d. Royal blue, powder blue, and white

3. Royals added black to their color scheme for the 2002 season.

   a. True
   b. False

4. Which of the following numbers is NOT retired by the Kansas City?

a. 5
b. 10
c. 15
d. 20

5. What uniform number does Alex Gordon currently wear as a member of the Royals?

   a. 3
   b. 4
   c. 7
   d. 9

6. What uniform number did Amos Otis wear during his time with the Royals?

   a. 23
   b. 24
   c. 25
   d. 26

7. George Brett's uniform number is retired by the Kansas City Royals.

   a. True
   b. False

8. George Scott, Nick Heath, and which other player are the only players in Kansas City Royals history to wear the uniform number 0?

   a. Tony Peña
   b. Terrance Gore
   c. Coco Crisp
   d. Terrence Long

9. Who is the only Royals player to have ever worn the uniform number 91?

    a. Jakob Junis
    b. Ryan O'Hearn
    c. Hideo Nomo
    d. Jake Newberry

10. During his time with the Kansas City Royals, Carlos Beltrán wore the uniform numbers 36 and 15.

    a. True
    b. False

11. What uniform number did Lorenzo Cain wear as a member of the Kansas City Royals?

    a. 3
    b. 4
    c. 5
    d. 6

12. What uniform number did Zack Greinke wear as a member of the Kansas City Royals?

    a. 13
    b. 21
    c. 23
    d. 32

13. Jeff Montgomery wore the uniform number 40 during his time with the Kansas City Royals.

    a. True
    b. False

14. What uniform number did John Mayberry wear as a member of the Kansas City Royals?

    a. 00
    b. 7
    c. 12
    d. 33

15. What uniform number did Mike Sweeney wear as a member of the Kansas City Royals?

    a. 10
    b. 17
    c. 27
    d. Both B and C

16. What uniform number did Johnny Damon wear as a member of the Kansas City Royals?

    a. 8
    b. 18
    c. 51
    d. Both B and C

17. During his time with the Kansas City Royals, Kevin Appier wore the uniform numbers 55 and which other number?

    a. 17
    b. 19
    c. 27
    d. 29

18. What uniform number does Salvador Pérez currently wear as a member of the Kansas City Royals?

    a. 3
    b. 13
    c. 23
    d. 33

19. What uniform number did Dan Quisenberry wear as a member of the Kansas City Royals?

    a. 28
    b. 29
    c. 40
    d. 47

20. Dennis Leonard wore the uniform number 22 during his time with the Kansas City Royals.

    a. True
    b. False

QUIZ ANSWERS

1. A – True
2. C – Royal blue, powder blue, gold, and white
3. A – True
4. C – 15
5. B – 4
6. D – 26
7. A – True
8. B – Terrance Gore
9. C – Hideo Nomo
10. A – True
11. D – 6
12. C – 23
13. B – False (Montgomery wore number 21.)
14. B – 7
15. D – Both B and C
16. D – Both B and C
17. A – 17
18. B – 13
19. B – 29
20. A – True

DID YOU KNOW?

1. The Kansas City Royals have retired four uniform numbers so far in franchise history: George Brett (number 5), Dick Howser (number 10), Frank White (number 20), and Jackie Robinson (number 42).
2. Carlos Hernandez is the only player in Royals franchise history so far to wear the uniform number 71.
3. Eric Skoglund is the only player in Royals franchise history so far to wear the uniform number 69.
4. During his time with the Kansas City Royals, Paul Splittorff wore the uniform numbers 25 and 34.
5. During his time with the Kansas City Royals, Bret Saberhagen wore the uniform numbers 31 and 18.
6. During his time with the Kansas City Royals, Larry Gura wore the uniform numbers 37 and 32.
7. Jackie Robinson's number 42 is retired by the Royals as well as the MLB as a whole. No Royals or MLB player will ever wear number 42 again. The Yankees' Mariano Rivera was the final player to wear it.
8. During his time with the Kansas City Royals, Charlie Leibrandt wore the uniform number 37.
9. During his time with the Kansas City Royals, Hal McRae wore the uniform number 11.
10. During his time with the Kansas City Royals, Freddie Patek wore the uniform numbers 37 and 2.

CHAPTER 3:

AMERICA'S PASTIME

QUIZ TIME!

1. How many total teams play in Major League Baseball?
   a. 15
   b. 20
   c. 30
   d. 33
2. Major League Baseball was founded in 1903.
   a. True
   b. False
3. Who is the current commissioner of Major League Baseball?
   a. Bart Giamatti
   b. Fay Vincent
   c. Bud Selig
   d. Rob Manfred

4. What year was the National League founded?

    a. 1870
    b. 1876
    c. 1903
    d. 1911

5. What year was the American League founded?

    a. 1888
    b. 1901
    c. 1903
    d. 1918

6. Major League Baseball is the second wealthiest professional sports league. Which league is the wealthiest?

    a. NBA
    b. NHL
    c. NFL
    d. MLS

7. The Major League Baseball headquarters is located in New York City.

    a. True
    b. False

8. How many games does each Major League Baseball team play per season?

    a. 92
    b. 122
    c. 162
    d. 192

9. In which two U.S. states is Major League Baseball's Spring Training held?

   a. California and Florida
   b. Arizona and Florida
   c. Arizona and California
   d. California and Arizona

10. How many stitches does a Major League Baseball baseball have?

   a. 98
   b. 100
   c. 108
   d. 110

11. Where is the National Baseball Hall of Fame located?

   a. Denver, Colorado
   b. Phoenix, Arizona
   c. Los Angeles, California
   d. Cooperstown, New York

12. All 30 Major League Baseball teams are located in the United States.

   a. True
   b. False

13. Which current Major League Baseball stadium is the oldest baseball stadium still in use?

   a. Angel Stadium
   b. Dodger Stadium
   c. Fenway Park
   d. Wrigley Field

14. Major League Baseball has the highest attendance of any sports league in the world.

    a. True
    b. False

15. Fill in the blank: Seventh Inning ______________ .

    a. Jog
    b. Song
    c. Shake
    d. Stretch

16. William Howard Taft was the first United States president to throw out the ceremonial first pitch at a Major League Baseball game.

    a. True
    b. False

17. It is a Major League Baseball rule that all umpires must wear __________ underwear in case they rip their pants.

    a. Tan
    b. Gray
    c. White
    d. Black

18. What year did the first Major League Baseball World Series take place?

    a. 1903
    b. 1905
    c. 1915
    d. 1920

19. Former Major League Baseball Commissioner Bart Giamatti is the father of actor Paul Giamatti.

    a. True
    b. False

20. The song traditionally played in the middle of the 7th inning at Major League Baseball games is called "Take Me Out to the Ballpark."

    a. True
    b. False

QUIZ ANSWERS

1. C – 30
2. A – True
3. D – Rob Manfred
4. B – 1876
5. B – 1901
6. C – NFL
7. A – True
8. C – 162
9. B – Arizona and Florida
10. C – 108
11. D – Cooperstown, New York
12. B – False (Just 29 out of 30; the Toronto Blue Jays are located in Canada.)
13. C – Fenway Park
14. A – True
15. D – Stretch
16. A – True
17. D – Black
18. A – 1903
19. A – True
20. B – False (The song is called "Take Me Out to the Ballgame.")

DID YOU KNOW?

1. The average lifespan of a baseball in a Major League Baseball game is 5-7 pitches. This means approximately 5-6 dozen baseballs are used in every Major League Baseball game.
2. The Boston Americans won the very first Major League Baseball World Series. They defeated the Pittsburgh Pirates in eight games. Today, the most games a World Series can go is seven.
3. The New York Yankees currently hold the most World Series titles in Major League Baseball, with 27 (as of the end of the 2020 MLB season).
4. Hot dogs are the most popular food item sold at Major League Baseball ballparks. Over 21 million hot dogs were sold at MLB stadiums in 2014.
5. The longest Major League Baseball game on record occurred on May 9, 1984, between the Chicago White Sox and Milwaukee Brewers. The game lasted eight hours, six minutes. The most innings played in a Major League Baseball game were 26 innings on May 1, 1920. The game was between the Brooklyn Dodgers and Boston Braves.
6. The mound to home plate distance at Major League Baseball ballparks is 60 feet, 6 inches.

7. Before they can be used in a Major League Baseball game, each MLB baseball is rubbed with a special mud to improve grip and reduce luster. This special mud comes from a specific, secret location in the state of New Jersey.
8. The fastest Major League Baseball game on record took place on September 28, 1919. The game between the New York Giants and Philadelphia Phillies took 51 minutes. An average MLB game is three hours.
9. The American League uses a designated hitter. A DH only hits and does not play in the field. In the National League, the pitcher hits instead of using a designated hitter. If an interleague game is being played, whether a DH is used or not is determined by which team is the home team. If the home team is from the American League, each team will use a DH. If the home team is from the National League, each team's pitcher will hit.
10. The distance between each of the four bases in Major League Baseball is 90 feet.

CHAPTER 4:

CATCHY NICKNAMES

QUIZ TIME!

1. What nickname does Kevin Appier go by?
   a. Ape
   b. App
   c. Pier
   d. KevApp
2. Amos Otis goes by the nickname "A.O."
   a. True
   b. False
3. Which of the following is NOT a nickname that the Royals as a team are often referred to as?
   a. The Blue Crew
   b. Boys in Blue
   c. The Crowns
   d. The Kings

4. What nickname does Alex Gordon go by?
    a. Flash Gordon
    b. The Don
    c. Gordo
    d. A Gor
5. What nickname did Dan Quisenberry go by?
    a. Q
    b. Quiz
    c. Berry
    d. Both A and B
6. Which nickname does Lorenzo Cain go by?
    a. Crunchwrap
    b. LoCain
    c. Cain and Able
    d. Both A and B
7. Kauffman Stadium is often referred to as "The K."
    a. True
    b. False
8. Which nickname does Salvador Pérez go by?
    a. Salpy
    b. Salvy
    c. El Receptor
    d. El Real
9. Which two nicknames did Freddie Patek go by during his playing career?

a. The Cricket / The Jackrabbit
b. The Cricket / The Giraffe
c. The Flea / The Cricket
d. The Flea / The Fly

10. What is former Royals' manager "Whitey"?

a. Lorrel Elvert Norman Herzog
b. Lorrel Norman Elvert Herzog
c. Dorrel Norman Elvert Herzog
d. Dorrel Elvert Norman Herzog

11. What nickname does Danny Duffy go by?

a. Cat
b. Bear
c. Tiger
d. Zebra

12. Billy Butler goes by the nickname "Country Breakfast."

a. True
b. False

13. Which nickname does Johnny Damon go by?

a. Dame
b. Henchman
c. JD
d. Caveman

14. What is former Royal Joe Randa's nickname?

a. The Clown
b. The Penguin

c. The Joker
d. The Riddler

15. Wally Joyner goes by the nickname "Wally World."

a. True
b. False

16. What nickname does Jose Lind go by?

a. Jumpin' Jose
b. Lindy
c. Chico
d. Hombre

17. Gary Gaetti's nicknames included "The Rat" and "G-Man."

a. True
b. False

18. What is Buck Martinez's full name?

a. Albert Jack Martinez
b. Jack Albert Martinez
c. Albert John Martinez
d. John Albert Martinez

19. What nickname does Lou Piniella go by?

a. Pinny
b. Sweet Lou
c. LVP
d. Sweet Pin

20. Jerry Adair went by the nickname "Casper the Friendly Ghost."

    a. True
    b. False

QUIZ ANSWERS

1. A – Ape
2. A – True
3. D – The Kings
4. C – Gordo
5. D – Both A and B
6. D – Both A and B
7. A – True
8. B – Salvy
9. C – The Flea / The Cricket
10. C – Dorrel Norman Elvert Herzog
11. B – Bear
12. A – True
13. D – Caveman
14. C – The Joker
15. A – True
16. C – Chico
17. A – True
18. D – John Albert Martinez
19. B – Sweet Lou
20. A – True

DID YOU KNOW?

1. Former Royal Mitch Williams went by the nickname "Wild Thing," but it had nothing to do with the baseball movie *Major League*. The nickname came from his wild pitching delivery.
2. Kevin McReynolds goes by the nickname "Big Mac."
3. David Cone goes by the nickname "Coney."
4. Eric Hosmer goes by the nicknames "Hoz" and "Papo."
5. Mike Moustakas goes by the nickname "Moose."
6. Alcides Escobar goes by the nickname "Esky."
7. Kendrys Morales goes by the nickname "Mo Mo."
8. Ben Zobrist goes by the nickname "Zorilla."
9. Jarrod Dyson goes by the nickname "Zoombiya."
10. Jason Vargas goes by the nickname "Vargy."

CHAPTER 5:

MULLET

QUIZ TIME!

1. What is George Brett's full name?
    a. Hank George Brett
    b. George Hank Brett
    c. Howard George Brett
    d. George Howard Brett
2. George Brett made his debut with the Kansas City Royals in 1973.
    a. True
    b. False
3. Where was George Brett born?
    a. Charleston, West Virginia
    b. Branson, Missouri
    c. Glen Dale, West Virginia
    d. Trenton, New Jersey
4. When was George Brett born?

a. May 15, 1950
b. May 15, 1953
c. March 15, 1950
d. March 15, 1953

5. George Brett is the only player to win a batting title in three different decades in MLB history.

a. True
b. False

6. How many MLB All-Star Games was George Brett named to over the course of his MLB career?

a. 10
b. 11
c. 12
d. 13

7. George Brett was drafted in which round of the 1971 MLB Draft?

a. 1st
b. 2nd
c. 3rd
d. 4th

8. George Brett played his entire MLB career with the Kansas City Royals.

a. True
b. False

9. What year was George Brett inducted into the National Baseball Hall of Fame?

a. 1978
b. 1980
c. 1999
d. 1989

10. What year was George Brett named American League MVP?

a. 1971
b. 1980
c. 1985
d. 1990

11. How many Silver Slugger Awards did George Brett win during his MLB career?

a. 1
b. 2
c. 3
d. 4

12. George Brett was named ALCS MVP in 1985.

a. True
b. False

13. How many times was George Brett named the American League batting champion during his MLB career?

a. 2
b. 3
c. 4
d. 5

14. George Brett won only one Gold Glove Award during his MLB career.

    a. True
    b. False

15. Which sitcom did George Brett appear on in 2018?

    a. The Big Bang Theory
    b. Brooklyn Nine-Nine
    c. Schitt's Creek
    d. Modern Family

16. How many home runs did George Brett hit over the course of his MLB career?

    a. 297
    b. 307
    c. 317
    d. 327

17. George Brett's career batting average is .305.

    a. True
    b. False

18. How many hits did George Brett hit over the course of his MLB career?

    a. 3,054
    b. 3,154
    c. 3,254
    d. 3,354

19. How many RBI did George Brett hit over the course of his MLB career?

    a. 1,596
    b. 1,496
    c. 1,396
    d. 1,296

20. George Brett stole 201 bases during his MLB career.

    a. True
    b. False

QUIZ ANSWERS

1. D – George Howard Brett
2. A – True
3. C – Glen Dale, West Virginia
4. B – May 15, 1953
5. A – True
6. D – 13
7. B – 2nd
8. A – True
9. C – 1999
10. B – 1980
11. C – 3
12. A – True
13. B – 3
14. A – True
15. D – Modern Family
16. C – 317
17. A – True
18. B – 3,154
19. A – 1,596
20. A – True

DID YOU KNOW?

1. George Brett is one of only four players to accumulate 3,000 hits, 300 home runs, and have a a career .300 batting average in MLB history (the others are Hank Aaron, Willie Mays, and Stan Musial).
2. George Brett threw out the ceremonial first pitch to Mike Napoli at the 2012 Major League Baseball All-Star Game.
3. After his retirement, George Brett became a vice president of the Royals. He has also worked as a coach, Spring Training instructor, interim batting coach, and a minor league instructor.
4. George Brett and his brother, Bobby own a baseball equipment and glove company called Brett Bros.
5. George Brett created the term the "Mendoza Line", which references a player who has a batting average below .200.
6. A photo in *National Geographic* showing George Brett signing baseballs for fans was the inspiration for Lorde's 2013 hit song "Royals."
7. George Brett was inducted into the Missouri Sports Hall of Fame in 1994.
8. George Brett was inducted into the National Baseball Hall of Fame with an impressive 98.2% of the vote.
9. George Brett's uniform number 5 was retired by the Royals on May 14, 1994.

10. In a 1983 game against the New York Yankees, George Brett hit a home run, but was called out because of too much pine tar on his bat. Brett stormed out of the dugout directly toward the umpire and had to be physically restrained by two other umpires and Dick Howser.

CHAPTER 6:

STATISTICALLY SPEAKING

QUIZ TIME!

1. George Brett currently holds the Kansas City Royals franchise record for the most home runs. How many home runs did he hit during his MLB career?
    a. 267
    b. 307
    c. 317
    d. 377
2. Pitcher Paul Splittorff has the most wins in Kansas City Royals franchise history, with 166.
    a. True
    b. False
3. Which pitcher holds the Kansas City Royals' record for most career shutouts thrown, with 23?
    a. Mark Gubicza
    b. Paul Splittorff
    c. Dennis Leonard
    d. Larry Gura

4. Which Kansas City Royals batter currently holds the single season record for strikeouts, with 178?
    a. Alex Gordon
    b. Steve Balboni
    c. Bo Jackson
    d. Jorge Soler
5. Which pitcher has the most strikeouts in Kansas City Royals franchise history, with 1,458?
    a. Bret Saberhagen
    b. Kevin Appier
    c. Mark Gubicza
    d. Paul Splittorff
6. Who has the most stolen bases in Kansas City Royals franchise history, with 612?
    a. Frank White
    b. Freddie Patek
    c. Willie Wilson
    d. Amos Otis
7. Jeff Montgomery holds the record for most saves in Kansas City Royals history, with 304.
    a. True
    b. False
8. Who holds the Kansas City Royals' record for being intentionally walked, with 229?
    a. John Mayberry
    b. George Brett

c. Hal McRae
d. Mike Sweeney

9. Which player holds the Kansas City Royals franchise record for home runs in a single season, with 48?

a. Steve Balboni
b. Mike Moustakas
c. Jorge Soler
d. Jermaine Dye

10. Which batter holds the single season Kansas City Royals record for hits, with 230?

a. Melky Cabrera
b. Whit Merrifield
c. Johnny Damon
d. Willie Wilson

11. Who holds the single season, Kansas City Royals record for double plays grounded into, with 32?

a. Cookie Rojas
b. Lou Piniella
c. Billy Butler
d. John Wathan

12. George Brett holds the record for the most sacrifice flies in Kansas City Royals all-time franchise history, with 120.

a. True
b. False

13. Mark Gubicza holds the Kansas City Royals franchise record for the number of wild pitches with how many?

a. 87
b. 97
c. 107
d. 117

14. Willie Wilson holds the Kansas City Royals' single season record for most triples. How many did he hit in his record 1985 season?

    a. 12
    b. 17
    c. 21
    d. 27

15. Which hitter has the most walks in Kansas City Royals franchise history, with 1,096?

    a. Mike Sweeney
    b. Hal McRae
    c. Amos Otis
    d. George Brett

16. Which Kansas City Royals hitter holds the all-time franchise record for best overall batting average at .306?

    a. George Brett
    b. Jose Offerman
    c. Mike Sweeney
    d. Johnny Damon

17. Amos Otis holds the Kansas City Royals' record for most runs scored, with 1,583.

    a. True
    b. False

18. George Brett holds the record for most plate appearances all time in Kansas City Royals franchise history. How many plate appearances did he make?

    a. 7,362
    b. 7,970
    c. 8,468
    d. 11,624

19. Which pitcher holds the Kansas City Royals franchise record for most saves in a single season, with 47?

    a. Joakim Soria
    b. Dan Quisenberry
    c. Jeff Montgomery
    d. Greg Holland

20. Paul Splittorff holds the Kansas City Royals franchise record for most losses, with 143.

    a. True
    b. False

QUIZ ANSWERS

1. C – 317
2. A – True
3. C – Dennis Leonard
4. D – Jorge Soler
5. B – Kevin Appier
6. C – Willie Wilson
7. A – True
8. B – George Brett
9. C – Jorge Soler (2019)
10. D – Willie Wilson (1980)
11. C – Billy Butler (2010)
12. A – True
13. C – 107
14. C – 21
15. D – George Brett
16. B – Jose Offerman
17. B – False (George Brett holds that record.)
18. D – 11,624
19. D – Greg Holland (2013)
20. A – True

DID YOU KNOW?

1. Paul Splittorff threw the most innings in Kansas City Royals franchise history, with 2,554.2. Coming in second is Mark Gubicza who threw 2,218.2 innings.

2. George Brett had the best single season batting average in Kansas City Royals franchise history at .390 in 1980. Coming in second is Mike Sweeney whose batting average was .340 in 2002.

3. Carlos Beltrán holds the Kansas City Royals franchise record for stolen base percentage with 87.70% accuracy. Willie Wilson holds the Kansas City Royals franchise record for stolen bases, with 612. Willie Wilson holds the Kansas City Royals franchise record for the most times caught stealing, with 119.

4. George Brett has the most extra-base hits in Kansas City Royals franchise history, with 1,119. Second on the list is Hal McRae with 681.

5. Steve Balboni holds the Kansas City Royals franchise record for at-bats per home run at 16.8. Essentially, what this means is that, on average, Balboni hit a home run about every 16-17 at-bats.

6. Ian Kennedy holds the Kansas City Royals franchise record for strikeouts per nine innings pitched at 8.363. Essentially, what this means is that, during his time with

the Royals, Kennedy recorded about 8-9 strikeouts in every nine innings that he pitched.

7. David DeJesus holds the single season Kansas City Royals record for the most hit by pitches with 23 in 2007. Jakob Junis holds the single season Kansas City Royals record for most batters hit with 15 in 2018.

8. George Brett holds the Kansas City Royals franchise record for career doubles hit, with 665. Second on the list is Hal McRae with 449.

9. Bret Saberhagen holds the Kansas City Royals' single season record for wins with 23 in 1989.

10. Two pitchers are tied for the Kansas City Royals' single season record for losses with 19 each. Those two pitchers are Darrell May (2004) and Paul Splittorff (1974).

CHAPTER 7:

THE TRADE MARKET

QUIZ TIME!

1. On December 9, 2012, the Kansas City Royals traded Wil Myers, Patrick Leonard, Mike Montgomery, and Jake Odorizzi to the Tampa Bay Rays for Wade Davis, Eliot Johnson, and which other player?

    a. Eric Hosmer
    b. Mike Moustakas
    c. James Shields
    d. Ervin Santana

2. On December 19, 2010, the Kansas City Royals traded cash, Yuniesky Betancourt, and which third player to the Milwaukee Brewers for Lorenzo Cain, Alcides Escobar, Jeremy Jefferies, and Jake Odorizzi?

    a. David DeJesus
    b. Zack Greinke
    c. Joakim Soria
    d. Willie Bloomquist

3. The Kansas City Royals have made 12 trades with the New York Yankees as of the end of the 2020 season.
   a. True
   b. False
4. On December 11, 1991, the Kansas City Royals traded Bill Pecota and which other player to the New York Mets for Kevin McReynolds, Gregg Jefferies, and Keith Miller.
   a. Brent Mayne
   b. Kevin Appier
   c. Jeff Montgomery
   d. Bret Saberhagen
5. The Kansas City Royals have only made eight trades with the Arizona Diamondbacks all time.
   a. True
   b. False
6. On November 30, 1972, the Kansas City Royals traded Roger Nelson and Richie Scheinblum to the which team for Hal McRae and Wayne Simpson?
   a. Cincinnati Reds
   b. Baltimore Orioles
   c. Los Angeles Dodgers
   d. Cleveland Indians
7. On March 27, 1987, the Kansas City Royals traded Chris Jelic and which player to the New York Mets for Ed Hearn, Rick Anderson, and Mauro Gozzo?
   a. Dennis Leonard
   b. Charlie Leibrandt

c. Bud Black
d. David Cone

8. On December 2, 1971, the Kansas City Royals traded Lance Clemons and Jim York to the Houston Astros for David Grangaard and which player?
   a. Lou Piniella
   b. Freddie Patek
   c. John Mayberry
   d. Cookie Rojas

9. On July 28, 2015, the Kansas City Royals traded Sean Manaea and Aaron Brooks to which team for Ben Zobrist?
   a. Arizona Diamondbacks
   b. Chicago Cubs
   c. Oakland A's
   d. Tampa Bay Rays

10. The Kansas City Royals have made only 10 trades with the Colorado Rockies all time.
    a. True
    b. False

11. On July 26, 2015, the Kansas City Royals traded Brandon Finnegan, Cody Reed, and John Lamb to the Cincinnati Reds for which player?
    a. Joe Blanton
    b. Danny Duffy
    c. Joba Chamberlain
    d. Johnny Cueto

12. The Kansas City Royals have made only 12 trades with the Miami/Florida Marlins all time.

    a. True
    b. False

13. How many trades have the Kansas City Royals made with the San Diego Padres all time?

    a. 7
    b. 11
    c. 18
    d. 21

14. The Kansas City Royals have made only six trades with the Philadelphia Phillies all time.

    a. True
    b. False

15. On February 15, 1988, the Kansas City Royals traded Van Snider to the Cincinnati Reds for which player?

    a. Steve Balboni
    b. Jeff Montgomery
    c. Willie Wilson
    d. Danny Tartabull

16. On February 5, 1983, the Kansas City Royals traded Cecil Fielder to which team for Leon Roberts?

    a. Detroit Tigers
    b. New York Yankees
    c. Toronto Blue Jays
    d. Cleveland Indians

17. On November 7, 2011, the Kansas City Royals traded Melky Cabrera to which team for Jonathan Sanchez and Ryan Verdugo?

    a. New York Yankees
    b. Pittsburgh Pirates
    c. Chicago White Sox
    d. San Francisco Giants

18. On April 6, 1995, the Kansas City Royals traded David Cone to which team for Chris Stynes, Tony Medrano, and David Sinnes?

    a. New York Yankees
    b. New York Mets
    c. Toronto Blue Jays
    d. Boston Red Sox

19. On July 30, 2004, the Kansas City Royals traded Jose Bautista to which team for Justin Huber?

    a. Atlanta Braves
    b. Pittsburgh Pirates
    c. Toronto Blue Jays
    d. New York Mets

20. The Kansas City Royals have made 11 trades with the Detroit Tigers all time.

    a. True
    b. False

QUIZ ANSWERS

1. C – James Shields
2. B – Zack Greinke
3. A – True
4. D – Bret Saberhagen
5. A – True
6. A – Cincinnati Reds
7. D – David Cone
8. C – John Mayberry
9. C – Oakland A's
10. A – True
11. D – Johnny Cueto
12. A – True
13. C – 18
14. A – True
15. B – Jeff Montgomery
16. C – Toronto Blue Jays
17. D – San Francisco Giants
18. C – Toronto Blue Jays
19. D – New York Mets
20. A – True

DID YOU KNOW?

1. On June 24, 2004, in a three-team trade, the Kansas City Royals traded Carlos Beltrán to the Houston Astros for Mark Teahen and John Buck (Octavio Dotel was traded to the A's from the Astros.).
2. At the trade deadline in 1999, the Kansas City Royals traded Kevin Appier to the Oakland A's for Jeff D'Amico, Brad Rigby, and Blake Stein.
3. On November 19, 2008, the Kansas City Royals traded Ramon Ramirez to the Boston Red Sox for Coco Crisp.
4. On October 28, 1996, the Kansas City Royals traded Mike Bovee and Mark Gubicza to the Anaheim Angels for Chili Davis.
5. On August 11, 2014, the Kansas City Royals traded Jason Adam to the Minnesota Twins for Josh Willingham.
6. At the trade deadline in 2006, the Kansas City Royals traded Matt Stairs to the Texas Rangers for Jose Diaz.
7. On January 6, 2017, the Kansas City Royals traded Jarrod Dyson to the Seattle Mariners for Nate Karns.
8. On October 31, 2012, the Kansas City Royals traded Brandon Sisk to the Los Angeles Angels for Ervin Santana and cash considerations.
9. On May 16, 1976, the Kansas City Royals traded Fran Healy to the New York Yankees for Larry Gura.

10. On June 13, 1970, the Kansas City Royals traded Fred Rico to the St. Louis Cardinals for Cookie Rojas.

CHAPTER 8:

DRAFT DAY

QUIZ TIME!

1. George Brett was drafted by the Kansas City Royals in the 2nd round of which MLB Draft?

   a. 1970
   b. 1971
   c. 1972
   d. 1973

2. With which overall pick in the 1st round of the 1987 MLB Draft, the Kansas City Royals selected Kevin Appier.

   a. 1st
   b. 2nd
   c. 9th
   d. 10th

3. In the 5th round of the 1965 MLB Draft, which team selected Amos Otis?

   a. Kansas City Royals
   b. Pittsburgh Pirates

c. New York Mets
d. Boston Red Sox

4. With which overall pick in the 1st round of the 1974 MLB Draft, the Kansas City Royals selected Willie Wilson?

    a. 1st
    b. 5th
    c. 16th
    d. 18th

5. In the 2nd round of which MLB Draft, the Kansas City Royals selected Mark Gubicza?

    a. 1979
    b. 1980
    c. 1981
    d. 1982

6. With which overall pick in the 1st round of the 2005 MLB Draft, the Kansas City Royals selected Alex Gordon?

    a. 1st
    b. 2nd
    c. 3rd
    d. 4th

7. Hal McRae was drafted in the 6th round of the 1965 MLB Draft by the Cincinnati Reds.

    a. True
    b. False

8. With which overall pick in the 1st round of the 2002 MLB Draft, the Kansas City Royals selected Zack Greinke.

a. 1st
b. 3rd
c. 6th
d. 9th

9. In the 17th round of the 2004 MLB Draft, which team selected Lorenzo Cain.

    a. Detroit Tigers
    b. Atlanta Braves
    c. Los Angeles Dodgers
    d. Milwaukee Brewers

10. Dennis Leonard was drafted by the Kansas City Royals in the 2nd round of the 1972 MLB Draft.

    a. True
    b. False

11. Carlos Beltrán was drafted in which round of the 1995 MLB Draft by the Kansas City Royals?

    a. 2nd
    b. 4th
    c. 7th
    d. 12th

12. Mike Sweeney was drafted by the Kansas City Royals in the 10th round in the 1991 MLB Draft.

    a. True
    b. False

13. In which round of the 1968 MLB Draft, the Kansas City Royals selected Paul Splittorff?

a. 10th
b. 15th
c. 20th
d. 25th

14. Charlie Leibrandt was drafted in the 9th round of the 1978 MLB Draft by which team?

    a. Atlanta Braves
    b. Texas Rangers
    c. Cincinnati Reds
    d. Los Angeles Dodgers

15. John Mayberry was drafted in the 1st round (6th overall) of the 1967 MLB Draft by which team?

    a. Houston Astros
    b. Toronto Blue Jays
    c. New York Yankees
    d. Kansas City Royals

16. Jeff Montgomery was drafted in the 9th round of the 1983 MLB Draft by which team?

    a. Chicago White Sox
    b. Philadelphia Phillies
    c. Baltimore Orioles
    d. Cincinnati Reds

17. Freddie Patek was drafted in the 22nd round of the 1965 MLB Draft by which team?

    a. California Angels
    b. Pittsburgh Pirates

c. Minnesota Twins
d. Washington Senators

18. Larry Gura was drafted in the 2nd round of the 1969 MLB Draft by which team?

 a. Seattle Pilots
 b. Montreal Expos
 c. New York Yankees
 d. Chicago Cubs

19. Vida Blue was drafted in the 2nd round of the 1967 MLB Draft by which team?

 a. San Francisco Giants
 b. Kansas City Athletics
 c. Boston Red Sox
 d. Pittsburgh Pirates

20. Danny Duffy was drafted by the Kansas City Royals in the 3rd round of the 2007 MLB Draft.

 a. True
 b. False

QUIZ ANSWERS

1. B – 1971
2. C – 9th
3. D – Boston Red Sox
4. D – 18th
5. C – 1981
6. B – 2nd
7. A – True
8. C – 6th
9. D – Milwaukee Brewers
10. A – True
11. A – 2nd
12. A – True
13. D – 25th
14. C – Cincinnati Reds
15. A – Houston Astros
16. D – Cincinnati Reds
17. B – Pittsburgh Pirates
18. D – Chicago Cubs
19. B – Kansas City Athletics
20. A – True

DID YOU KNOW?

1. Whit Merrifield was drafted in the 9th round of the 2010 MLB Draft by the Kansas City Royals.
2. Wally Joyner was drafted in the 3rd round of the 1983 MLB Draft by the California Angels.
3. Johnny Damon was drafted in the 1st round (35th overall) of the 1992 MLB Draft by the Kansas City Royals.
4. Eric Hosmer was drafted in the 1st round (3rd overall) of the 2008 MLB Draft by the Kansas City Royals.
5. John Buck was drafted in the 7th round of the 1998 MLB Draft by the Houston Astros.
6. Mike Moustakas was drafted in the 1st round (2nd overall) of the 2007 MLB Draft by the Kansas City Royals.
7. Billy Butler was drafted in the 1st round (14th overall) of the 2004 MLB Draft by the Kansas City Royals.
8. Bo Jackson was drafted in the 4th round of the 1986 MLB Draft by the Kansas City Royals.
9. Jason Kendall was drafted in the 1st round (23rd overall) of the 1992 MLB Draft by the Pittsburgh Pirates.
10. Brent Mayne was drafted in the 1st round (13th overall) of the 1989 MLB Draft by the Kansas City Royals.

CHAPTER 9:

ODDS & ENDS

QUIZ TIME!

1. In a high school football game, former Royal Johnny Damon suffered his first sports concussion from which NFL star?
   a. Ronnie Lott
   b. Michael Strahan
   c. Troy Polamalu
   d. Warren Sapp
2. Jeremy Giambi is the brother of fellow former MLB player Jason Giambi.
   a. True
   b. False
3. Which BRAVO reality show has Johnny Damon appeared on twice?
   a. Vanderpump Rules
   b. Below Deck
   c. Southern Charm
   d. The Real Housewives of Beverly Hills

4. Cookie Rojas's son, Victor, is a play-by-play announcer for which MLB team?
    a. Minnesota Twins
    b. Toronto Blue Jays
    c. Los Angeles Angels
    d. Texas Rangers
5. Zack Greinke is a minority owner of a which franchise?
    a. In-N-Out
    b. Dunkin' Donuts
    c. Ben & Jerry's
    d. Chipotle
6. After his MLB career came to an end, Dan Quisenberry started a new career as a ________________.
    a. Car mechanic
    b. Poet
    c. Real estate agent
    d. Chef
7. Hal McRae's son, Brian, played for the Kansas City Royals as well.
    a. True
    b. False
8. David DeJesus's wife, Kim, was a contestant on which reality show?
    a. Big Brother
    b. Survivor
    c. The Amazing Race
    d. American Idol

9. Former Royal Bud Black is currently the manager of which team?
    a. Cleveland Indians
    b. Toronto Blue Jays
    c. San Diego Padres
    d. Colorado Rockies
10. Lou Piniella made a cameo in which baseball film?
    a. Moneyball
    b. Little Big League
    c. Fever Pitch
    d. The Rookie
11. Which TV sitcom did Danny Tartabull make an appearance on?
    a. Married… with Children
    b. Seinfeld
    c. The Fresh Prince of Bel Air
    d. Both A and B
12. John Mayberry's son, John Mayberry Jr., played in the MLB from 2009 to 2015.
    a. True
    b. False
13. How are former Royals Onix Concepcion and Jose Lind related?
    a. Brothers
    b. Cousins
    c. Brothers-in-law
    d. Uncle and nephew

14. Bo Jackson won the Heisman Trophy in 1985.

    a. True
    b. False

15. Former Royal Clint Hurdle went on to manage the Colorado Rockies which other team?

    a. Cincinnati Reds
    b. St. Louis Cardinals
    c. Pittsburgh Pirates
    d. New York Mets

16. Jason Kendall wrote a book, Throwback: A Big-League Catcher Tells How the Game Is Really Played, which was released in May 2014.

    a. True
    b. False

17. Joba Chamberlain made an appearance on an episode of which popular television show?

    a. The Great Food Truck Race
    b. Top Chef
    c. Man v. Food
    d. Hell's Kitchen

18. Hunter Dozier and Brian Dozier are ___________________.

    a. Brothers
    b. Cousins
    c. Father and son
    d. Not related

19. Which musician's famous song "Royals" was inspired by the Kansas City Royals?

    a. Ariana Grande
    b. Maren Morris
    c. Lorde
    d. Pink

20. A species of weevil, Sicoderus bautistai, was named after Jose Bautsita in 2018.

    a. True
    b. False

QUIZ ANSWERS

1. D – Warren Sapp
2. A – True
3. B – Below Deck
4. C – Los Angeles Angels
5. D – Chipotle
6. B – Poet
7. A – True
8. C – The Amazing Race
9. D – Colorado Rockies
10. B – Little Big League
11. D – Both A and B
12. A – True
13. B – Cousins
14. A – True
15. C – Pittsburgh Pirates
16. A – True
17. C – *Man v. Food*
18. D – Not related
19. C – Lorde
20. A – True

DID YOU KNOW?

1. In July 2017, former Royal Coco Crisp became the head coach of the baseball team at Shadow Hills High School in Indio, California. In 2019, he joined the Oakland Athletics Radio Network part time as a color analyst.
2. During the Houston Astros' 2017 championship season, former Royal Carlos Beltrán was said to be the leader of their illegal sign stealing system. He was hired to be the new manager of the New York Mets but quit the job before the season started as a result of his role in the cheating scheme.
3. During the 2013 season, Alcides Escobar sprayed Salvador Pérez with a Victoria's Secret women's perfume. He had four hits in that game, which led Pérez to continue wearing that perfume during games as his good-luck charm. He made the switch to 212 VIP cologne by Carolina Herrera in 2014.
4. On January 24, 2020, Salvador Pérez was became an American citizen. He took the oath of citizenship at the Royals' FanFest.
5. Ervin Santana was born Johan Ramon Santana, and used that name until 2003. He changed his name to avoid having the same name as fellow MLB pitcher Johan Santana. There is no reason for the name Ervin, he just came up with it and thought it sounded good.

6. Until March 2011, the MLB spelled Kendrys Morales's first name as "Kendry" by mistake.
7. Bob Lemon became the first American League manager to win a World Series after taking on the role in the middle of a MLB season.
8. Joe Blanton and his wife own a three-acre vineyard in St. Helena, California. They produce cabernet sauvignon.
9. Matt Stairs was elected to the Canadian Baseball Hall of Fame in 2015.
10. Salvador Pérez is known for giving a Gatorade shower (aka a "Salvy Splash") to his teammates during postgame TV interviews.

CHAPTER 10:

OUTFIELDERS

QUIZ TIME!

1. Jermaine Dye played five seasons with the Kansas City Royals. Which of the teams below did he NOT play for during his 14-season career?
   a. Oakland Athletics
   b. Atlanta Braves
   c. Chicago White Sox
   d. Seattle Mariners
2. Alex Gordon has won two Platinum Gold Glove Awards.
   a. True
   b. False
3. How many Silver Slugger Awards did Willie Wilson win during his 19-season MLB career?
   a. 0
   b. 1
   c. 2
   d. 3

4. Carlos Beltrán was named the 1999 American League Rookie of the Year.

   a. True
   b. False

5. How many MLB All-Star Games was Johnny Damon named to in his 18-year MLB career?

   a. 1
   b. 2
   c. 4
   d. 6

6. Which of the following teams did Danny Tartabull NOT play for during his 14-season MLB career?

   a. New York Yankees
   b. Philadelphia Phillies
   c. Seattle Mariners
   d. New York Mets

7. Lorenzo Cain played seven seasons with the Kansas City Royals.

   a. True
   b. False

8. Which of the following teams did David DeJesus NOT play for during his 13-season MLB career?

   a. Tampa Bay Rays
   b. Chicago Cubs
   c. San Diego Padres
   d. Oakland A's

9. Bo Jackson was named the All-Star Game MVP in which year?

    a. 1987
    b. 1989
    c. 1990
    d. 1993

10. How many seasons did Jarrod Dyson play for the Kansas City Royals?

    a. 3
    b. 5
    c. 7
    d. 8

11. How many Gold Glove Awards did Jeff Francoeur win during his 12-season MLB career?

    a. 0
    b. 1
    c. 2
    d. 3

12. Raul Ibanez spent 19 seasons in the MLB.

    a. True
    b. False

13. How many MLB All-Star Games was Alex Rios named to during his 12-season MLB career?

    a. 5
    b. 4
    c. 3
    d. 2

14. Which of the following teams did Coco Crisp NOT play for during his 15-season MLB career?

    a. Oakland A's
    b. Boston Red Sox
    c. Atlanta Braves
    d. Cleveland Indians

15. Which of the following teams did Willie Bloomquist NOT play for during his 14-season MLB career?

    a. Seattle Mariners
    b. Arizona Diamondbacks
    c. Tampa Bay Rays
    d. Cincinnati Reds

16. How many MLB All-Star Games was Jose Bautista named to during his 15-season MLB career?

    a. 3
    b. 4
    c. 5
    d. 6

17. How many seasons did Matt Stairs play for the Kansas City Royals?

    a. 2
    b. 3
    c. 4
    d. 5

18. How many seasons did Clint Hurdle play for the Kansas City Royals?

a. 2
b. 3
c. 4
d. 5

19. Alex Gordon has been named to how many MLB All-Star Games?

a. 1
b. 2
c. 3
d. 4

20. Jermaine Dye was named to two MLB All-Star Games during his 14-season MLB career.

a. True
b. False

QUIZ ANSWERS

1. D – Seattle Mariners
2. A – True
3. C – 2
4. A – True
5. B – 2
6. D – New York Mets
7. A – True
8. C – San Diego Padres
9. B – 1989
10. C – 7
11. B – 1
12. A – True
13. D – 2
14. C – Atlanta Braves
15. C – Tampa Bay Rays
16. D – 6
17. B – 3
18. D – 5
19. C – 3
20. A – True

DID YOU KNOW?

1. Alex Gordon has played for the Kansas City Royals since the 2007 season. He is a three-time MLB All-Star, has won eight Gold Glove Awards and two Platinum Glove Awards, and is a 2015 World Series champion.
2. Jermaine Dye spent five seasons of his 14-season MLB career with the Kansas City Royals. He also played for the Oakland Athletics, Chicago White Sox, and Atlanta Braves. He is a two-time MLB All-Star, Gold Glove Award winner, Silver Slugger Award winner, 2005 World Series champion, and World Series MVP.
3. Willie Wilson spent 15 seasons of his 19-season MLB career with the Kansas City Royals. He also played for the Oakland Athletics and Chicago Cubs. He is a two-time MLB All-Star, Gold Glove Award winner, two-time Silver Slugger Award winner, batting title champion, and 1985 World Series champion.
4. Johnny Damon spent six seasons of his 18-season MLB career with the Kansas City Royals. He also played for the Oakland Athletics, Boston Red Sox, New York Yankees, Tampa Bay Rays, Cleveland Indians, and Detroit Tigers. He is a two-time MLB All-Star and two-time World Series champion.
5. Carlos Beltrán spent seven seasons of his 20-season MLB career with the Kansas City Royals. He also played for the

New York Mets, New York Yankees, St. Louis Cardinals, Houston Astros, Texas Rangers, and San Francisco Giants. He is a nine-time MLB All-Star, three-time Gold Glove Award winner, two-time Silver Slugger Award winner, 1999 American League Rookie of the Year, and 2017 World Series champion.

6. Danny Tartabull spent five seasons of his 14-season MLB career with the Kansas City Royals. He also played for the New York Yankees, Seattle Mariners, Philadelphia Phillies, Oakland A's, and Chicago White Sox. He is a one-time MLB All-Star.

7. Lorenzo Cain spent seven seasons of his MLB career with the Kansas City Royals. He currently plays for the Milwaukee Brewers. So far in his career, he is a two-time MLB All-Star, Gold Glove Award winner, ALCS MVP, and 2015 World Series champion.

8. Jeff Francoeur spent three seasons of his 12-season MLB career with the Kansas City Royals. He also played for the San Diego Padres, Atlanta Braves, New York Mets, San Francisco Giants, Philadelphia Phillies, Texas Rangers, and Miami Marlins. He is a one-time Gold Glove Award winner.

9. Jose Bautista spent one season of his 15-season MLB career with the Kansas City Royals. He also played for the Toronto Blue Jays, Pittsburgh Pirates, New York Mets, Tampa Bay Devil Rays, Philadelphia Phillies, Atlanta Braves, and Baltimore Orioles. He is a six-time MLB All-Star and three-time Silver Slugger Award winner.

10. Coco Crisp spent one season of his 15-season MLB career with the Kansas City Royals. He also played for the Oakland Athletics, Cleveland Indians, and Boston Red Sox. He is a 2007 World Series champion.

CHAPTER 11:

INFIELDERS

QUIZ TIME!

1. How many seasons did Eric Hosmer play for the Kansas City Royals?

    a. 5
    b. 6
    c. 7
    d. 8

2. Alcides Escobar was named the 2015 ALCS MVP.

    a. True
    b. False

3. Mike Moustakas has been named to how many MLB All-Star Games?

    a. 2
    b. 3
    c. 4
    d. 5

4. How many Gold Glove Awards did Frank White win during his 18-season MLB career?

   a. 5
   b. 6
   c. 7
   d. 8

5. How many MLB All-Star Games was George Brett named to during his 21-season MLB career?

   a. 10
   b. 11
   c. 13
   d. 15

6. How many seasons did Mike Sweeney play for the Kansas City Royals?

   a. 11
   b. 13
   c. 14
   d. 16

7. Freddie Patek played his entire 14-season MLB career with the Kansas City Royals.

   a. True
   b. False

8. How many MLB All-Star Games was John Mayberry named to during his 15-season MLB career?

   a. 2
   b. 3

c. 6
d. 10

9. How many seasons did Omar Infante play for the Kansas City Royals?

a. 2
b. 3
c. 4
d. 5

10. How many MLB All-Star Games was Kevin Seitzer named to during his 12-season MLB career?

a. 0
b. 1
c. 2
d. 3

11. Which of the following teams did Wally Joyner NOT play for during his 16-season MLB career?

a. San Diego Padres
b. California Angels
c. Atlanta Braves
d. Texas Rangers

12. Gary Gaetti won four Gold Glove Awards during his 20-season MLB career.

a. True
b. False

13. Which Kansas City Royals infielder was named the 2003 American League Rookie of the Year?

a. Matt Stairs
b. Ángel Berroa
c. Mark Teahen
d. Joe McEwing

14. How many MLB All-Star Games was Cookie Rojas named to during his 16-season MLB career?

a. 1
b. 3
c. 5
d. 7

15. In what year did Mark Grudzielanek win his sole Gold Glove Award?

a. 2005
b. 2006
c. 2007
d. 2008

16. Whit Merrifield was drafted by the Kansas City Royals in 2010.

a. True
b. False

17. How many MLB All-Star Games was Gregg Jefferies named to during his 14-season MLB career?

a. 1
b. 2
c. 3
d. 4

18. Which of the following teams did Alberto Callaspo NOT play for during his 10-season MLB career?

    a. Los Angeles Angels
    b. Oakland A's
    c. Los Angeles Dodgers
    d. Miami Marlins

19. How many Silver Slugger Awards did Dean Palmer win during his 14-season MLB career?

    a. 4
    b. 3
    c. 2
    d. 1

20. Jose Offerman was named to two MLB All-Star Games during his 15-season MLB career.

    a. True
    b. False

QUIZ ANSWERS

1. C – 7
2. A – True
3. B – 3
4. D – 8
5. C – 13
6. B – 13
7. B – False (He played for the Royals, Pittsburgh Pirates, and California Angels.)
8. A – 2
9. B – 3
10. C – 2
11. D – Texas Rangers
12. A – True
13. B – Ángel Berroa
14. C – 5
15. B – 2006
16. A – True
17. B – 2
18. D – Miami Marlins
19. C – 2
20. A – True

DID YOU KNOW?

1. Eric Hosmer spent seven seasons of his MLB career with the Kansas City Royals. He currently plays for the San Diego Padres. Hosmer is a one-time MLB All-Star, four-time Gold Glove Award winner, one-time Silver Slugger Award winner, All-Star Game MVP, and 2015 World Series champion.
2. Alcides Escobar spent eight seasons of his 11-season MLB career with the Kansas City Royals. He also played for the Milwaukee Brewers. He is a one-time MLB All-Star, one-time Gold Glove Award winner, ALCS MVP, and 2015 World Series champion.
3. Mike Moustakas spent eight seasons of his MLB career with the Kansas City Royals. He currently plays for the Cincinnati Reds. He has also played for the Milwaukee Brewers. Moustakas is a three-time MLB All-Star and 2015 World Series champion.
4. Frank White spent his entire 18-season MLB career with the Kansas City Royals. He is a five-time MLB All-Star, eight-time Gold Glove Award winner, one-time Silver Slugger Award winner, ALCS MVP, and 1985 World Series champion.
5. George Brett spent his entire 21-season MLB career with the Kansas City Royals. He is a member of the National Baseball Hall of Fame, MVP, thirteen-time MLB All-Star,

three-time Silver Slugger Award winner, Gold Glove Award winner, three-time batting title champion, ALCS MVP, Major League Player of the Year, and 1985 World Series champion.

6. Mike Sweeney spent 13 seasons of his 16-season MLB career with the Kansas City Royals. He also played for the Seattle Mariners, Philadelphia Phillies, and Oakland A's. He is a five-time MLB All-Star.

7. Freddie Patek spent nine seasons of his 14-season MLB career with the Kansas City Royals. He also played for the Pittsburgh Pirates and California Angels. He is a three-time MLB All-Star.

8. John Mayberry spent six seasons of his 15-season MLB career with the Kansas City Royals. He also played for the Toronto Blue Jays, Houston Astros, and New York Yankees. He is a two-time MLB All-Star.

9. Wally Joyner spent four seasons of his 16-season MLB career with the Kansas City Royals. He also played for the California Angels, San Diego Padres, and Atlanta Braves. He is a one-time MLB All-Star.

10. Cookie Rojas spent eight seasons of his 16-season MLB career with the Kansas City Royals. He also played for the Cincinnati Reds, Philadelphia Phillies, and St. Louis Cardinals. He is a five-time MLB All-Star. He went on to manage the California Angels and Florida Marlins.

CHAPTER 12:

PITCHERS & CATCHERS

QUIZ TIME!

1. What year did Kevin Appier win the American League pitching title?
   a. 1990
   b. 1992
   c. 1993
   d. 1995
2. Bret Saberhagen won two Cy Young Awards during his 16-season MLB career.
   a. True
   b. False
3. Over the course of his 14-season MLB career, Mark Gubicza played 13 seasons with the Kansas City Royals and one season with which other team?
   a. New York Yankees
   b. Chicago Cubs
   c. San Diego Padres
   d. Anaheim Angels

4. How many Silver Slugger Awards has Zack Greinke ?
    a. 0
    b. 1
    c. 2
    d. 3
5. How many MLB All-Star Games was Dan Quisenberry named to during his 12-season MLB career?
    a. 2
    b. 3
    c. 4
    d. 5
6. How many seasons did John Buck spend with the Kansas City Royals?
    a. 3
    b. 4
    c. 6
    d. 8
7. Dennis Leonard played his entire 12-season MLB career with the Kansas City Royals.
    a. True
    b. False
8. Over the course of his 15-season career, Paul Splittoroff played for the Kansas City Royals and the which other team?
    a. Houston Astros
    b. Oakland A's

c. Los Angeles Dodgers
d. None of the above; he played his entire career with the Royals.

9. Which of the following teams did Charlie Leibrandt NOT play for during his 14-season MLB career?

   a. Cincinnati Reds
   b. Houston Astros
   c. Atlanta Braves
   d. Texas Rangers

10. How many MLB All-Star Games was Jeff Montgomery named to during his 13-season MLB career?

    a. 0
    b. 2
    c. 3
    d. 5

11. Over the course of his 16-year MLB career, pitcher Larry Gura played for the Royals, Chicago Cubs, and which other team?

    a. San Francisco Giants
    b. Pittsburgh Pirates
    c. Cleveland Indians
    d. New York Yankees

12. Salvador Pérez was the 2015 World Series MVP.

    a. True
    b. False

13. How many seasons did Brent Mayne spend with the Kansas City Royals?

    a. 5
    b. 7
    c. 9
    d. 12

14. How many Gold Glove Awards did Jim Sundberg win during his 16-season MLB career?

    a. 4
    b. 6
    c. 7
    d. 8

15. Which of the following teams did Jason Kendall NOT play for during his 15-season MLB career?

    a. Pittsburgh Pirates
    b. Arizona Diamondbacks
    c. Oakland A's
    d. Chicago Cubs

16. David Cone won five World Series championships during his 17-season MLB career.

    a. True
    b. False

17. How many seasons did Mike Macfarlane spend with the Kansas City Royals?

    a. 9
    b. 10

c. 11
d. 12

18. How many MLB All-Star Games was Vida Blue named to during his 17-year MLB career?

a. 5
b. 6
c. 7
d. 8

19. Over the course of his 17-season MLB career, Buck Martinez played for the Kansas City Royals, Milwaukee Brewers, and which other team?

a. Los Angeles Dodgers
b. Texas Rangers
c. St. Louis Cardinals
d. Toronto Blue Jays

20. Danny Duffy has played his entire MLB career with the Kansas City Royals.

a. True
b. False

QUIZ ANSWERS

1. C – 1993
2. A – True
3. D – Anaheim Angels
4. C – 2
5. B – 3
6. C – 6
7. A – True
8. D – None of the above; he played his entire career with the Royals.
9. B – Houston Astros
10. C – 3
11. D – New York Yankees
12. A – True
13. C – 9
14. B – 6
15. B – Arizona Diamondbacks
16. A – True
17. C – 11
18. B – 6
19. D – Toronto Blue Jays
20. A – True

DID YOU KNOW?

1. Kevin Appier spent 13 seasons of his 16-season MLB career with the Kansas City Royals. He also played for the Anaheim Angels, Oakland A's, and New York Mets. He is a one-time MLB All-Star, 1993 American League pitching title winner, and 2002 World Series champion.

2. Bret Saberhagen spent eight seasons of his 16-season MLB career with the Kansas City Royals. He also played for the Boston Red Sox, Colorado Rockies, and New York Mets. He is a three-time MLB All-Star, two-time Cy Young Award winner, Gold Glove Award winner, 1985 World Series MVP, 1989 American League pitching title winner, and 1985 World Series champion.

3. Mark Gubicza spent 13 seasons of his 14-season MLB career with the Kansas City Royals. He also played for the Anaheim Angels. He is a two-time MLB All-Star and 1985 World Series champion.

4. Zack Greinke spent seven seasons of his MLB career with the Kansas City Royals. He has also played for the Arizona Diamondbacks, Los Angeles Angels, Milwaukee Brewers, and Los Angeles Dodgers. He currently plays for the Houston Astros. he is a Cy Young Award winner, six-time MLB All-Star, six-time Gold Glove Award winner, two-time Silver Slugger Award winner, and two-time pitching title champion.

5. Dan Quisenberry spent 10 seasons of his 12-season MLB career with the Kansas City Royals. He also played for the St. Louis Cardinals and San Francisco Giants. He is a three-time MLB All-Star, five-time Rolaids Reliever of the Year, and 1985 World Series champion.
6. So far, Salvador Pérez has spent his entire MLB career with the Kansas City Royals. he is a six-time MLB All-Star, five-time Gold Glove Award winner, three-time Silver Slugger Award winner, 2015 World Series champion, and 2015 World Series MVP.
7. David Cone spent three seasons of his 17-season MLB career with the Kansas City Royals. He also played for the New York Mets, New York Yankees, Toronto Blue Jays, and Boston Red Sox. He is a Cy Young Award winner, five-time MLB All-Star, and five-time World Series champion.
8. Vida Blue spent two seasons of his 17-season MLB career with the Kansas City Royals. He also played for the Oakland A's and San Francisco Giants. He is a six-time MLB All-Star, MVP, Cy Young Award winner, 1971 American League pitching title champion, and three-time World Series champion.
9. Jeff Montgomery spent 12 seasons of his 13-season MLB career with the Kansas City Royals. He also played for the Cincinnati Reds. He is a three-time MLB All-Star and Rolaids Reliever of the Year Award winner.

10. There have been four no-hitters in Kansas City Royals franchise history. Royals' pitchers who have thrown no-hitters include: Steve Busby (2), Jim Colborn, and Bret Saberhagen.

CHAPTER 13:

WORLD SERIES

QUIZ TIME!

1. How many World Series championships have the Kansas City Royals won in franchise history?

    a. 0
    b. 1
    c. 2
    d. 3

2. How many AL pennants have the Kansas City Royals won?

    a. 1
    b. 2
    c. 3
    d. 4

3. Which team did the Kansas City Royals face in the 1980 World Series?

    a. Atlanta Braves
    b. Philadelphia Phillies

c. St. Louis Cardinals
d. Houston Astros

4. Which team did the Kansas City Royals face in the 1985 World Series?

    a. San Diego Padres
    b. New York Mets
    c. Los Angeles Dodgers
    d. St. Louis Cardinals

5. Which team did the Kansas City Royals face in the 2014 World Series?

    a. San Francisco Giants
    b. St. Louis Cardinals
    c. Los Angeles Dodgers
    d. Cincinnati Reds

6. Which team did the Kansas City Royals face in the 2015 World Series?

    a. Los Angeles Dodgers
    b. San Francisco Giants
    c. New York Mets
    d. St. Louis Cardinals

7. The 1980 World Series went six games.

    a. True
    b. False

8. How many games did the 1985 World Series go?

    a. 4
    b. 5

c. 6
d. 7

9. How many games did the 2014 World Series go?

    a. 4
    b. 5
    c. 6
    d. 7

10. How many games did the 2015 World Series go?

    a. 4
    b. 5
    c. 6
    d. 7

11. Who was the manager of the Kansas City Royals during the 1980 World Series?

    a. Bob Lemon
    b. Whitey Herzog
    c. Dick Howser
    d. Jim Frey

12. Dick Howser was the manager of the Kansas City Royals during the 1985 World Series.

    a. True
    b. False

13. Who was the manager of the Kansas City Royals during the 2014 and 2015 World Series?

    a. Mike Matheny
    b. Tony Muser

c. Ned Yost
d. Hal McRae

14. Which Kansas City Royals pitcher got the win in Game 7 of the 1985 World Series?

    a. Bud Black
    b. Bret Saberhagen
    c. Dan Quisenberry
    d. Charlie Leibrandt

15. Which Kansas City Royals pitcher got the win in Game 5 of the 2015 World Series?

    a. Luke Hochevar
    b. Wade Davis
    c. Danny Duffy
    d. Johnny Cueto

16. The Kansas City Royals won Game 5 to clinch the 2015 World Series championship at Citi Field in Queens, New York.

    a. True
    b. False

17. How many home runs did Alex Gordon hit in the 2015 World Series?

    a. 0
    b. 1
    c. 3
    d. 4

18. How many home runs did Amos Otis hit in the 1980 World Series?

    a. 1
    b. 2
    c. 3
    d. 4

19. How many RBI did Frank White collect during the 1985 World Series?

    a. 3
    b. 4
    c. 5
    d. 6

20. Eric Hosmer struck out eight times during the 2014 World Series.

    a. True
    b. False

QUIZ ANSWERS

1. C – 2 (1985 and 2015)
2. D – 4 (1980, 1985, 2014, and 2015)
3. B – Philadelphia Phillies
4. D – St. Louis Cardinals
5. A – San Francisco Giants
6. C – New York Mets
7. A – True
8. D – 7
9. D – 7
10. B – 5
11. D – Jim Frey
12. A – True
13. C – Ned Yost
14. B – Bret Saberhagen
15. A – Luke Hochevar
16. A – True
17. B – 1
18. C – 3
19. D – 6
20. A – True

DID YOU KNOW?

1. Game 6 of the 1985 World Series to this day is the most-watched game in World Series history. It had a TV audience of 54.9 million.
2. In 1980, the Kansas City Royals became the second expansion team, and the first from the American League, to appear in the World Series. In 1985, the Royals became the first American League expansion team to win a World Series.
3. The 1980 World Series was the played entirely on artificial turf. The 1980 World Series was also the first World Series since 1920 played between two teams who had never won a World Series Championship.
4. The 1985 World Series was the second all-Missouri World Series. The first was an all-St. Louis series in 1944 between the Cardinals and Browns (now the Baltimore Orioles).
5. In the 1985 World Series, the Royals became the first team in MLB history to win the World Series after losing Games 1 and 2 at home.
6. In 2014, the Royals became the first team in MLB history to begin a World Series with an 8-0 record in that postseason.
7. In 2015, the Royals became the first team since the Oakland Athletics in 1989 to win the World Series after losing it the season before.

8. The 2015 World Series was the first World Series to be played between two expansion teams (Royals and Mets).
9. In 2015, the Royals became the first team in World Series history to start three pitchers who were born outside of the United States (Yordano Ventura, Edison Volquez, and Johnny Cueto).
10. In the 1989 film *Back to the Future Part II*, the Chicago Cubs are depicted as the 2015 World Series champions. When the Royals won in 2015, Back to the Future's Twitter acknowledged it by tweeting that there was a "disruption in the space-time continuum." The Cubs won the World Series the following season, in 2016, ending their 108-year championship drought.

CHAPTER 14:

HEATED RIVALRIES

QUIZ TIME!

1. Which team does NOT play in the American League Central with the Kansas City Royals?
    a. Chicago White Sox
    b. Minnesota Twins
    c. Milwaukee Brewers
    d. Cleveland Indians
2. The Kansas City Royals were a part of the American League West Division from 1969 to 1993.
    a. True
    b. False
3. Which team below was once a member of the AL Central Division?
    a. Cincinnati Reds
    b. Pittsburgh Pirates
    c. Milwaukee Brewers
    d. Chicago Cubs

4. What current American League Central team has the most AL Central championships?

   a. Chicago White Sox
   b. Detroit Tigers
   c. Minnesota Twins
   d. Cleveland Indians

5. What is a series with intrastate rival the St. Louis Cardinals called?

   a. Missouri Series
   b. I-70 Series
   c. Freeway Series
   d. Battle of Missouri

6. What year did the Royals and Cardinals have their first meeting?

   a. 1969
   b. 1975
   c. 1985
   d. 1995

7. From 1976 to 1980, the Royals faced the New York Yankees four times in five years in the American League Championship Series (ALCS).

   a. True
   b. False

8. The Royals have two World Series championships. How many do the Chicago White Sox have?

   a. 2
   b. 3

c. 4
d. 5

9. The Royals have two World Series championships. How many do the Cleveland Indians have?

    a. 0
    b. 1
    c. 2
    d. 3

10. The Royals have two World Series championships. How many do the Detroit Tigers have?

    a. 1
    b. 2
    c. 3
    d. 4

11. The Royals have two World Series championships. How many do the Minnesota Twins have?

    a. 0
    b. 1
    c. 2
    d. 3

12. The St. Louis Cardinals currently have the most I-70 Series wins.

    a. True
    b. False

13. Which player has NOT played for both the Royals and the Chicago White Sox?

a. Melky Cabrera
b. Nori Aoki
c. Jermaine Dye
d. Bo Jackson

14. Which player has NOT played for both the Royals and the Cleveland Indians?

a. Kevin Appier
b. Mike Aviles
c. Johnny Damon
d. Coco Crisp

15. Which player has NOT played for both the Royals and the Detroit Tigers?

a. Omar Infante
b. Rusty Meacham
c. Mark Gubicza
d. Matt Stairs

16. The Chicago White Sox and Kansas City Royals are the only teams from the AL Central who have won the World Series since the1994 league realignment.

a. True
b. False

17. Which player has NOT played for both the Royals and the Minnesota Twins?

a. Gary Gaetti
b. Ervin Santana
c. Kendrys Morales
d. Charlie Leibrandt

18. Which player has NOT played for both the Royals and the St. Louis Cardinals?

    a. Dan Quisenberry
    b. Larry Gura
    c. Cookie Rojas
    d. Carlos Beltrán

19. How many AL Central division titles did the Milwaukee Brewers win before they moved to the NL Central?

    a. 0
    b. 1
    c. 2
    d. 3

20. The Kansas City Royals have the least amount of AL Central division titles at one.

    a. True
    b. False

QUIZ ANSWERS

1. C – Milwaukee Brewers
2. A – True
3. C – Milwaukee Brewers
4. D – Cleveland Indians (10)
5. B – I-70 Series
6. C – 1985 (in the World Series)
7. A – True (70-60)
8. B – 3
9. C – 2
10. D – 4
11. D – 3
12. A – True (68-49)
13. B – Nori Aoki
14. A – Kevin Appier
15. C – Mark Gubicza
16. A – True
17. D – Charlie Leibrandt
18. B – Larry Gura
19. A – 0
20. A – True

DID YOU KNOW?

1. The Cleveland Indians have the most American League Central division championships, with 10. The Minnesota Twins have eight, the Detroit Tigers have four, the Chicago White Sox have three, and Kansas City Royals have one. The Milwaukee Brewers, formerly of the AL Central, did not win a division title during their time in the AL Central. The most recent AL Central division champions are the Minnesota Twins (2020). The Royals have not won the AL Central since 2015. The 2015 season was the first and only season where the Royals won the AL Central… so far.
2. A series between the Kansas City Royals and St. Louis Cardinals is often referred to as the "I-70 Series," but it is also sometimes called the "Show-Me Series." The Royals and Cardinals are 241 miles apart via I-70. Kauffman Stadium is further west than Busch Stadium.
3. All members of the AL Central have won a World Series championship, which is only true for two divisions in the MLB. In the AL Central, each team has captured at least two World Series championships.
4. Current Kansas City Royals manager Mike Matheny played for the rival St. Louis Cardinals as a catcher for five seasons. He also was manager of the Cardinals from 2012 to 2018.

5. "I hated everyone on the Yankees, I really did. I hated 'em all, back in that era." – George Brett

6. Rick Ankiel, Carlos Beltrán, Pat Borders, Jose Cardenal, Orlando Cepeda, Octavio Dotel, Mike Fiore, Gary Gaetti, Mark Grudzielanek, Greg Holland, Clint Hurdle, Jon Jay, Greg Jefferies, Mark Littell, Mike MacDougal, Brandon Moss, Darrell Porter, Dan Quisenberry, Cookie Rojas, Trevor Rosenthal, Lonnie Smith, and Jamey Wright have all played for both the Kansas City Royals and the St. Louis Cardinals.

7. Mike Armstrong, Mike Aviles, Bud Black, Pat Borders, Melky Cabrera, Jose Cardenal, Jamey Carroll, Joba Chamberlain, Bruce Chen, Dave Clark, Coco Crisp, Johnny Damon, Mark Grudzielanek, Jeremy Guthrie, Brandon Moss, Lou Piniella, Bip Roberts, Kevin Seitzer, and Jamey Wright have all played for both the Kansas City Royals and the Cleveland Indians.

8. Homer Bailey, Pat Borders, Steve Braun, Drew Butera, Jamey Carroll, Chili Davis, Gary Gaetti, Greg Gagne, Liam Hendricks, Philip Humber, Kendrys Morales, Jose Offerman, Ervin Santana, Danny Valencia, and Josh Willingham have all played for both the Kansas City Royals and the Minnesota Twins.

9. Mike Aviles, Joba Chamberlain, Al Cowens, Johnny Damon, Octavio Dotel, Neftali Feliz, Kirk Gibson, A.J. Hinch, Omar Infante, Gregg Jefferies, Rusty Meacham, Bob Melvin, Jim Nettles, Carlos Pena, Joe Randa, Bip Roberts,

Trevor Rosenthal, Joakim Soria, and Matt Stairs have all played for both the Kansas City Royals and the Detroit Tigers.

10. Floyd Bannister, Emilio Bonifacio, Pat Borders, Melky Cabrera, Octavio Dotel, Jermaine Dye, Jarrod Dyson, Chris Getz, Kelvin Herrera, Philip Humber, Bo Jackson, Jon Jay, Mike MacDougal, Bob Melvin, Alex Rios, Ervin Santana, James Shields, Joakim Soria, Danny Tartabull, and Mark Teahen have all played for both the Kansas City Royals and the Chicago White Sox.

CHAPTER 15:

THE AWARDS SECTION

QUIZ TIME!

1. Which Kansas City Royals player won the American League MVP Award in 1980?
   a. Willie Wilson
   b. Hal McRae
   c. George Brett
   d. Larry Gura
2. Tony Peña is the only Royals manager to ever win the American League Manager of the Year Award.
   a. True
   b. False
3. Which Kansas City Royals pitcher won the Cy Young Award in 1994?
   a. Kevin Appier
   b. David Cone
   c. Mark Gubicza
   d. None of the above

4. Which Kansas City Royals player most recently won the American League Rookie of the Year Award?

    a. Lou Piniella
    b. Bob Hamelin
    c. Carlos Beltrán
    d. Ángel Berroa

5. What year did the Kansas City Royals as a team win the Wilson Defensive Player of the Year Award?

    a. 2012
    b. 2013
    c. 2014
    d. Both A and B

6. Which Kansas City Royals player won a Silver Slugger Award in 2016?

    a. Alex Gordon
    b. Kendrys Morales
    c. Salvador Pérez
    d. Eric Hosmer

7. No Kansas City Royals player has ever won the MLB Home Run Derby.

    a. True
    b. False

8. Which Kansas City Royals player was named the DHL Hometown Hero (Voted by MLB fans as the most outstanding player in franchise history)?

    a. George Brett
    b. Bret Saberhagen

c. Carlos Beltrán
d. Frank White

9. Who was the first Kansas City Royals player to win an American League Gold Glove Award?

    a. Al Cowens
    b. Frank White
    c. Amos Otis
    d. Willie Wilson

10. Who was the first Kansas City Royals player to win a Silver Slugger Award?

    a. George Brett
    b. Willie Wilson
    c. Hal McRae
    d. Both A and B

11. Which Kansas City Royals pitcher won a Cy Young Award in 2009?

    a. Joakim Soria
    b. Zack Greinke
    c. Bruce Chen
    d. Rob Tejada

12. George Brett is the only Kansas City Royals player to win the AL MVP Award.

    a. True
    b. False

13. Lou Piniella was named the American League Rookie of the Year in what year?

a. 1969
b. 1970
c. 1971
d. 1972

14. Who was named the MLB All-Star Game MVP in 1989?

a. Bret Saberhagen
b. George Brett
c. Bo Jackson
d. Kevin Appier

15. In 2014, Alex Gordon and which other player, won Wilson Defensive Player of the Year Award?

a. Mike Moustakas
b. Lorenzo Cain
c. Eric Hosmer
d. Salvador Pérez

16. Dan Quisenberry has won more Rolaids Relief Man of the Year Awards than any other player in baseball history.

a. True
b. False

17. Which Kansas City Royals player was named the 2016 MLB All-Star Game MVP?

a. Jarrod Dyson
b. Alex Gordon
c. Alcides Escobar
d. Eric Hosmer

18. Which Kansas City Royals player won a Silver Slugger Award in 1995?

    a. Wally Joyner
    b. Gary Gaetti
    c. Johnny Damon
    d. Mike Sweeney

19. How many Gold Glove Awards did Johnny Damon win during his time with the Kansas City Royals?

    a. 0
    b. 1
    c. 2
    d. 3

20. George Brett NEVER won a Gold Glove Award.

    a. True
    b. False

QUIZ ANSWERS

1. C – George Brett
2. A – True (2003)
3. B – David Cone
4. D – Ángel Berroa (2003)
5. D – Both A and B
6. C – Salvador Pérez
7. A – True
8. A – George Brett
9. C – Amos Otis
10. D – Both A and B (1980)
11. B – Zack Greinke
12. A – True
13. A – 1969
14. C – Bo Jackson
15. B – Lorenzo Cain
16. A – True
17. D – Eric Hosmer
18. B – Gary Gaetti
19. A – 0
20. B – False (1, 1985)

DID YOU KNOW?

1. The Kansas City Royals have three different pitchers who have been named Cy Young Award winners in franchise history: Bret Saberhagen (1985 and 1989), David Cone (1994), and Zack Greinke (2009).
2. The Kansas City Royals have had 10 different players win Silver Slugger Awards in franchise history: George Brett (3), Willie Wilson (2), Hal McRae, Frank White, Gary Gaetti, Dean Palmer, Billy Butler, Kendrys Morales, Salvador Pérez (2), and Eric Hosmer.
3. The Kansas City Royals have four different players who have been named American League Rookie of the Year in franchise history: Lou Piniella (1969), Bob Hamelin (1994), Carlos Beltrán (1999), and Ángel Berroa (2003).
4. The Kansas City Royals have had 13 different players win Gold Glove Awards in franchise history: Amos Otis (3), Frank White (8), Al Cowens, Willie Wilson, George Brett, Bret Saberhagen, Bob Boone, Jermaine Dye, Mark Grudzielanek, Alex Gordon (7), Salvador Pérez (5), Eric Hosmer (3), and Alcides Escobar.
5. Only one Kansas City Royals player has ever been named MVP in franchise history: George Brett in 1980.
6. George Brett is on the Kansas City Sports Walk of Stars.
7. Frank White won the 1980 ALCS MVP Award, George Brett won the 1985 ALCS MVP Award, Lorenzo Cain won

the 2014 ALCS MVP Award, and Alcides Escobar won the 2015 ALCS MVP Award.

8. Bret Saberhagen won the 1985 World Series MVP Award. Salvador Pérez won the 2015 World Series MVP Award.
9. In 2015, Wade Davis won the Esurance MLB Award for Best Postseason Major Leaguer.
10. Dan Quisenberry and Jeff Montgomery are the only two Kansas City Royals pitchers to ever win the Rolaids Relief Man of the Year Award. Quisenberry won it four times during his tenure in K.C.

CHAPTER 16:

K.C.

QUIZ TIME!

1. Before Jackie Robinson broke the color barrier in the MLB, he played for which Kansas City team, as part of the Negro Leagues?
   a. Grays
   b. Eagles
   c. Stars
   d. Monarchs
2. Kansas City has more barbeque restaurants per capita than any other city in the United States.
   a. True
   b. False
3. Which former U.S. President owned a Kansas City haberdashery before he got into politics?
   a. Calvin Coolidge
   b. Harry S. Truman
   c. William McKinley
   d. Lyndon B. Johnson

4. Which chocolate brand's corporate campus is located in Kansas City?

    a. Russell Stover
    b. Ghirardelli
    c. Cadbury
    d. Hershey's

5. Which celebrity is NOT from Kansas City?

    a. Ed Asner
    b. Eric Stonestreet
    c. Robert Downey Jr.
    d. Don Cheadle

6. Which Kansas City team was a professional ice hockey team in the NHL from 1974 to 1976?

    a. Devils
    b. Sharks
    c. Ducks
    d. Scouts

7. Kansas City has over 200 fountains, giving it the nickname The City of Fountains.

    a. True
    b. False

8. What is the name of Kansas City's NFL team?

    a. Kansas City 49ers
    b. Kansas City Chiefs
    c. Kansas City Cowboys
    d. Kansas City Broncos

9. What is the name of Kansas City's MLS team?
   a. Sporting Kansas City
   b. KC FC
   c. Kansas City Union
   d. Kansas City Earthquakes
10. Which Kansas City team in the NBA played in K.C. from 1972 to 1985, before the team moved to Sacramento, California, in 1985?
    a. Warriors
    b. Kings
    c. Clippers
    d. Pistons
11. What is the name of the Chiefs' current stadium?
    a. Ford Field
    b. Levi's Stadium
    c. Arrowhead Stadium
    d. FedEx Field
12. The Oakland A's played in Kansas City (as the Kansas City Athletics) from 1955 to 1967.
    a. True
    b. False
13. What is the name of Sporting Kansas City's current stadium?
    a. Audi Field
    b. Children's Mercy Park
    c. Lumen Field
    d. Red Bull Field

14. What is the population of Kansas City (as of 2020)?

    a. 1,686,000
    b. 1,786,000
    c. 1,886,000
    d. 1,986,000

15. How many Super Bowl championships have the Kansas City Chiefs won (as of the end of 2020)?

    a. 0
    b. 1
    c. 2
    d. 3

16. Kansas City ignored Prohibition altogether.

    a. True
    b. False

17. How many times has Sporting Kansas City won the MLS Cup (as of the end of 2020)?

    a. 0
    b. 1
    c. 2
    d. 3

18. What is Kansas City International Airport's code?

    a. KCI
    b. MCI
    c. KCA
    d. KCI

19. What is the named of the first outdoor shopping district in the United States that opned in Kansas City in 1922?

    a. Sawgrass Mill Plaza
    b. Galleria Plaza
    c. Shops at Columbus Circle
    d. Country Club Plaza

20. Kansas City is the largest city in Missouri by both population and area.

    a. True
    b. False

QUIZ ANSWERS

1. D – Monarchs
2. A – True
3. B – Harry S. Truman
4. A – Russell Stover
5. C – Robert Downey Jr.
6. D – Scouts
7. A – True
8. B – Kansas City Chiefs
9. A – Sporting Kansas City
10. B – Kings
11. C – Arrowhead Stadium
12. A – True
13. B – Children's Mercy Park
14. A – 1,686,000
15. C – 2
16. A – True
17. C – 2
18. B – MCI
19. D – Country Club Plaza
20. A – True

DID YOU KNOW?

1. The scoreboard at Arrowhead Stadium was the first to have instant replay.
2. Ernest Hemingway worked as a reporter for the *Kansas City Star* from 1917 to 1918.
3. Walt Disney opened his first animation studio, called Laugh-O-Gram Studios, in Kansas City. Disney took drawing classes at the Kansas City Art Institute while in elementary school.
4. Joyce Hall, founder of Hallmark Cards, started out selling postcards out of a shoebox in Kansas City.
5. Swope Park in Kansas City is more than double the size of New York City's famous Central Park.
6. Kansas City has the second most boulevards in the world. Paris, France, has the most.
7. Kansas City is only a three-hour flight from both U.S. coasts.
8. The American Jazz Museum in Kansas City was the first museum in the United States dedicated solely to jazz music.
9. The Negro Leagues Baseball Museum in Kansas City displays the history of the professional African American baseball leagues, which were founded in Kansas City in 1920.

10. Union Station in Kansas City is the second-largest train station in the United States, behind only the famed Grand Central Station in New York.

CHAPTER 17:

SMOOTH

QUIZ TIME!

1. What is Frank White's full name?
    a. Frank James White Jr.
    b. Frank White Jr.
    c. Frank Joseph White
    d. Frank Ryan White
2. Frank White played his entire MLB career with the Kansas City Royals.
    a. True
    b. False
3. Where was Frank White born?
    a. Greenwood, Mississippi
    b. Jackson, Mississippi
    c. Vicksburg, Mississippi
    d. Greenville, Mississippi
4. When was Frank White born?

a. February 4, 1950
b. February 4, 1953
c. September 4, 1950
d. September 4, 1955

5. Frank White was named the 1980 ALCS MVP.

   a. True
   b. False

6. How many years did Frank White spend with the Kansas City Royals?

   a. 15
   b. 16
   c. 18
   d. 20

7. What year did the Kansas City Royals retire Frank White's uniform number 20?

   a. 1993
   b. 1995
   c. 1997
   d. 1999

8. In 2016, Frank White was elected as a county executive of Jackson County in Missouri.

   a. True
   b. False

9. What year was Frank White inducted into the Kansas City Royals Hall of Fame?

a. 1991
b. 1992
c. 1995
d. 1997

10. What is the title of Frank White's 2012 autobiography?

a. One Man's Dream: My Town, My Team, My Time
b. Forever Royal: My Town, My Team, My Time
c. One Royal's Dream: My Town, My Team, My Time
d. Forever Dream: My Town, My Team, My Time

11. How many MLB All-Star Games was Frank White named to during his career?

a. 2
b. 3
c. 4
d. 5

12. A bronze statue of Frank White was dedicated outside of Kauffman Stadium in 2004.

a. True
b. False

13. How many Gold Glove Awards did Frank White win over the course of his MLB career?

a. 5
b. 7
c. 8
d. 9

14. Frank White NEVER won a Silver Slugger Award.

a. True
b. False

15. What is Frank White's career batting average?

a. .245
b. .255
c. .265
d. .275

16. What year was Frank White inducted into the Missouri Sports Hall of Fame?

a. 1990
b. 1992
c. 1994
d. 1997

17. Frank White and George Brett set an MLB record by appearing in 1,914 games together.

a. True
b. False

18. How many home runs did Frank White hit over the course of his MLB career?

a. 150
b. 160
c. 170
d. 180

19. How many RBI did Frank White collect over the course of his MLB career?

a. 856
b. 866
c. 876
d. 886

20. Frank White won a World Series championship with the Royals in 1985.

a. True
b. False

QUIZ ANSWERS

1. B – Frank White Jr.
2. A – True
3. D – Greenville, Mississippi
4. C – September 4, 1950
5. A – True
6. C – 18
7. B – 1995
8. A – True
9. C – 1995
10. A – One Man's Dream: My Town, My Team, My Time
11. D – 5
12. A – True
13. C – 8
14. B – False (1, 1986)
15. B – .255
16. C – 1994
17. A – True
18. B – 160
19. D – 886
20. A – True

DID YOU KNOW?

1. Frank White won six consecutive Gold Glove Awards from 1977 to 1982. He won eight in his career.
2. Frank White is one of only three MLB players, along with Ron Washington and U L Washington, who were products of the Royals Academy.
3. In 2008, Frank White worked for FSN Kansas City as a color commentator on Royals TV broadcasts and as an analyst on the *Royals Live* postgame show.
4. Frank White ran for the Jackson County legislature in 2014 as a Democrat.
5. Frank White made his MLB debut with the Royals on June 12, 1973.
6. Frank White made his final MLB appearance with the Royals on September 30, 1990.
7. Until Frank White, the only other second baseman to hit in the cleanup spot in a World Series was Jackie Robinson.
8. Frank White went by the nicknames "Smooth" and "Hoover."
9. Frank White finished his career with 2,006 total hits.
10. Frank White finished his career with 178 stolen bases.

CHAPTER 18:

SABES

QUIZ TIME!

1. Where was Bret Saberhagen born?

    a. Peoria, Illinois
    b. Chicago Heights, Illinois
    c. Carmel, Indiana
    d. Fort Wayne, Indiana

2. Bret Saberhagen was inducted into the Kansas City Royals Hall of Fame in 2005.

    a. True
    b. False

3. Bret Saberhagen was drafted in which round of the 1982 MLB Draft by the Kansas City Royals?

    a. 1st
    b. 4th
    c. 9th
    d. 19th

4. How many no-hitters did Bret Saberhagen throw during his MLB career?

    a. 0
    b. 1
    c. 2
    d. 3

5. How many MLB All-Star Games was Bret Saberhagen named to during his MLB career?

    a. 3
    b. 6
    c. 9
    d. 10

6. How many Cy Young Awards did Bret Saberhagen win during his MLB career?

    a. 2
    b. 4
    c. 6
    d. 8

7. Bret Saberhagen played his entire MLB career with the Kansas City Royals.

    a. True
    b. False

8. Bret Saberhagen was the American League ERA Leader in which year?

    a. 1985
    b. 1987

c. 1989
d. 1991

9. Bret Saberhagen led the MLB in wins in which year?
   a. 1986
   b. 1989
   c. 1992
   d. 2000

10. How many Gold Glove Awards did Bret Saberhagen win during his MLB career?
    a. 0
    b. 1
    c. 2
    d. 3

11. What other sport did Bret Saberhagen play in high school?
    a. Badminton
    b. Basketball
    c. Tennis
    d. Football

12. Bret Saberhagen was named the 1985 World Series MVP.
    a. True
    b. False

13. How many strikeouts did Bret Saberhagen record during his MLB career?
    a. 1,515
    b. 1,615

c. 1,715
d. 1,815

14. What is Bret Saberhagen's career ERA?

a. 3.44
b. 3.34
c. 3.24
d. 3.14

15. What is Bret Saberhagen's career win-loss record?

a. 137-107
b. 147-117
c. 157-107
d. 167-117

16. In 1982, as a senior in high school, Bret Saberhagen pitched a no-hitter in the Los Angeles city championship game, which was played at Dodger Stadium.

a. True
b. False

17. How many wins did Bret Saberhagen record in his 1989 MLB leading season?

a. 21
b. 22
c. 23
d. 25

18. Bret Saberhagen won two Cy Young Awards during his MLB career, his first being in which year and his second in 1989?

a. 1984
b. 1985
c. 1986
d. 1988

19. Bret Saberhagen led the American League in ERA in 1989. What was his ERA for that season?

a. 2.36
b. 2.26
c. 2.16
d. 2.06

20. Bret Saberhagen is a member of the National Baseball Hall of Fame.

a. True
b. False

QUIZ ANSWERS

1. B – Chicago Heights, Illinois
2. A – True
3. D – 19th
4. B – 1 (August 26, 1991)
5. A – 3
6. A – 2
7. B – False (He played for the Royals, New York Mets, Colorado Rockies, and Boston Red Sox.)
8. C – 1989
9. B – 1989
10. B – 1 (1989)
11. D – Football
12. A – True
13. C – 1,715
14. B – 3.34
15. D – 167-117
16. A – True
17. C – 23
18. B – 1985
19. C – 2.16
20. B – False

DID YOU KNOW?

1. Bret Saberhagen appeared as himself in the 1994 Brendan Fraser movie *The Scout*. Saberhagen also appeared in a 1994 episode of *Married… with Children*.
2. Bret Saberhagen attended high school at Grover Cleveland High School in Reseda, California.
3. Bret Saberhagen made his MLB debut on April 4, 1984, with the Royals against the New York Yankees.
4. Bret Saberhagen played his final MLB game on August 7, 2001, with the Boston Red Sox against the Oakland A's.
5. Over the course of his MLB career, Bret Saberhagen pitched 2,562.2 innings.
6. Bret Saberhagen started 371 games during his MLB career.
7. Bret Saberhagen recorded one save in his MLB career.
8. On August 26, 1991, Bret Saberhagen pitched a no-hitter against the Chicago White Sox by a score of 7-0 at Kauffman Stadium. This is currently the latest no-hitter thrown by a Royal.
9. During his playing career, Bret Saberhagen developed a pattern of successful seasons in odd-numbered years (1985, 1987, 1989, 1991) and poor performance seasons in even-numbered years.
10. Bret Saberhagen claims that if he were voted into the National Baseball Hall of Fame, he would not attend the

ceremony because he believes Pete Rose should be inducted as well.

CONCLUSION

Learn anything new? Now you truly are the ultimate Royals fan! Not only did you learn about the Crowns of the modern era, but you also expanded your knowledge back to the early days of the franchise.

You learned about the Royals' origins and their history. You learned about the history of their uniforms and jersey numbers. You identified some famous quotes and read some of the craziest nicknames of all time. You learned more about the legendary George Brett. You also learned about the smooth Frank White and powerhouse pitcher Bret Saberhagen. You were amazed by Royals' stats and recalled some of the most infamous Royals trades and draft picks of all time. You broke down your knowledge by outfielders, infielders, pitchers, and catchers. You looked back on the Royals' championship, playoff feats and the awards that came before, during, and after them. You also learned about the Royals' fiercest rivalries inside and outside their division.

Every team in the MLB has a storied history, but the Royals have one of the most memorable of all. They have won two World Series championships with the backing of their devoted fans. Being the ultimate Royals fan takes knowledge and a whole lot of patience, which you tested with this book. Whether you knew every answer or were stumped by several questions, you learned some of the most interesting history that the game of baseball has to offer.

The deep history of the Kansas City Royals franchise represents what we all love about the game of baseball, the heart, the determination, the tough times, and the unexpected moments. Plus, the players that inspire us and encourage us to do our best, because even if you get knocked down, there is always another game and another day.

With players like Salvador Pérez, Alex Gordon, and Hunter Dozier, the future for the Royals continues to look bright. They have a lot to prove, but there is no doubt that this franchise will continue to be one of the most competitive teams in Major League Baseball year after year.

It's a new decade, which means there is a clean slate, ready to continue writing the history of the Kansas City Royals. The ultimate Royals fan cannot wait to see what's to come for their beloved boys in blue.

Made in the USA
Columbia, SC
27 October 2023

25075578R00085